Good Times
with Our Friends

1954 Edition

by DOROTHY BARUCH *and* ELIZABETH MONTGOMERY

WILLIAM S. GRAY, *Reading Director*

Illustrated by Eleanor Campbell

HEALTH AND PERSONAL DEVELOPMENT PROGRAM

CURRICULUM FOUNDATION SERIES
REG. U. S. PAT. OFF.

Scott, Foresman and Company

CHICAGO   ATLANTA   DALLAS   SAN FRANCISCO   NEW YORK

STORIES

Good Times at Home

Good Times at the Farm

Good Times with Friends

For permission to adapt and use copyrighted material, grateful acknowledgment
is made to D. Appleton-Century Company for "Ready for Breakfast" from
"Sleepy Sally" and for "The Birthday Dinner" from "Cakes for Dinner," both
in *Sally Does It* by Dorothy Walter Baruch and Elizabeth Rider Montgomery.

Good Times
at
Home

Sally Gets Up

Mother said, "Come, Sally.
Wake up, Sally.
Wake up! Wake up!"

Sally did not wake up.
She did not see Mother.
And she did not get up.

Jane said, "Get up, Sally.
Come to breakfast.
Wake up! Wake up!"

Sally did not wake up.
She did not see Jane.
And she did not get up.

Dick said, "Sally, Sally.

Wake up! Wake up!

We want to eat.

We want to eat breakfast."

Sally did not wake up.

She did not see Dick.

And she did not get up.

Spot went to Sally.

"Bow-wow, bow-wow!" he said.

"Bow-wow, bow-wow!"

Sally did wake up.

She did see Spot.

And she did get up.

Dick and Jane laughed.

"Oh, Sally," said Dick.

"Spot can make you get up."

Sally Helps Spot

"Look, Sally," said Dick.

"Jane and I are ready.

We are ready for breakfast."

Jane said, "Come, Sally.

I will help you get ready.

I will wash you."

"No, no," said Sally.

"I can wash.

I do not want you to wash me.

You and Dick can go down.

You can go down to breakfast.

And I can get ready."

Dick went to breakfast.

Jane went to breakfast.

Sally did not go.

"Bow-wow" said Spot.

"Oh, Spot," said Sally.

"You are not ready.

You are not ready for breakfast.

Here, Spot.

Come to Sally.

I will wash you now.

I will help you get ready."

Jane came up to get Sally.

Sally said, "Look, Jane.

Spot is not ready for breakfast.

I will wash Spot now.

I will get Spot ready."

"Oh, Sally," said Jane.

"You are funny.

You and I wash for breakfast.

But we do not wash Spot."

13

Ready for Breakfast

Jane said, "Oh, Sally.

Breakfast is ready now.

But you are not ready.

Mother wants you to come.

I will help you."

Sally said, "No, no, Jane.

Do not help me.

I can get ready.

I will come down soon."

Jane went down to breakfast.

Mother said, "Oh, Jane.

Did you help Sally?"

Jane said, "No, Mother.

I did not help Sally.

She did not want me to help.

She will come down soon."

Soon Sally came to breakfast.

"Look, look," said Sally.

"I can get ready for breakfast."

"Oh, oh," laughed Father.

"Oh, Sally," laughed Mother.

"Sally is ready," said Dick.

"Yes, yes," laughed Jane.

"Sally is ready."

Eat It and See

"What is this?" said Sally.

"I do not like it."

Dick said, "It is something good.
Eat it and see.
You will like it."

"No," said Sally.

"I will not like it.
And I do not want it."

Mother said, "Here, Sally.

This is good to eat.

Dick and Jane like it.

Father and I like it.

You will like it, too."

Sally said, "No, no.

I will not like it.

And I do not want it."

Father said, "Eat it and see."

Sally said, "I will see.
I will eat a little."
And she did.

"Oh," laughed Jane.
"See Sally eat it.
Sally likes it."

"Yes," said Sally.
"I do like it.
It is good."
And Sally laughed, too.

Spot and the Cars

Mother said, "Oh, Dick.

I want milk for Sally.

Please go and get the milk.

Please go and get it now."

Jane said, "I will go with Dick."

Sally said, "I will go with Dick."

"Bow-wow," said Spot.

"Oh, oh," laughed Mother.

"Spot wants to go with Dick, too."

"Away we go," said Dick.

"One, two, three, four.

Jane and Sally.

Spot and I.

One, two, three, four.

Away we go to get milk.

Away, away."

21

Jane said, "Look, look.

It is red.

We can not go now.

Stop, Dick and Sally.

Stop, Spot.

See the cars go.

We do not want to get hurt."

Spot did not stop.

Away he went.

"Here, Spot," said Dick.

"You can not go now.

You will get hurt."

Sally said, "Come here, Spot."

Jane said, "Come here, Spot."

But Spot did not stop.

"Oh, my!" said Dick.

"See where Spot is.

See the cars go.

Spot will get hurt!"

Sally said, "Look now, Dick.

See the cars stop.

See the cars stop for Spot.

He will not get hurt now."

Milk Is Good

Sally said, "Oh, Mother.

I like this lunch.

This is a good lunch."

Mother said, "Yes, Sally.

It is a good lunch.

The cookies are good.

And the milk is good, too.

Milk is good for you.

It will make you big."

In came Puff.

Sally said, "Puff is little.

Milk will make Puff big.

"Oh, Puff," said Sally.

"You can have some milk.

You are little now.

Milk will make you big.

Milk is a good lunch for you.

Here is some milk."

Sally saw Tim.

She said, "Here, Tim.

You can have lunch, too.

You are little.

Milk will make you big.

Here is some milk for you."

"Oh, Sally," said Mother.

"My funny little Sally.

Milk is good for you.

And milk is good for Puff.

But milk is not good for Tim."

What Sally Saw

Mother said, "Come, Sally.
You ate a big lunch.
Now I will wash you."

"Please, Mother," said Sally.
"Please do not wash me now.
I want to go out and play.
I want to play with my boat.
My pretty blue boat."

Mother laughed and laughed.

She said, "Come here, Sally.

Come and see something funny."

Sally went to Mother.

"What is it?" she said.

"Where is something funny?

What do you want me to see?"

"Look, Sally," said Mother.

"This is what I want you to see.

Guess who it is.

Is this a pretty Sally?

A pretty Baby Sally?"

Sally said, "No, no, Mother.

This is a funny Sally.

Not a pretty Sally.

Wash the funny Sally.

Please wash me now."

And Mother did.

Ready for Play

Sally said, "I ate my lunch.

I went to sleep.

Now I can go out.

Now I can go out and play.

I can play with my blue boat.

My pretty blue boat.

Now I can go out and play."

Sally saw Dick and Jane.

She said, "See my blue boat.

My pretty blue boat.

I can go out and play with it.

Here is the yellow boat.

Here is the white boat.

Will you come and play, too?"

"Yes, Sally," said Dick and Jane.

"We will get ready.

We will go out and play, too.

We will have some fun."

Dick put on something.
Jane put on something.

"Come, Sally," said Jane.
"You have the blue boat.
I can have the white boat.
Dick can have the yellow boat.
Now we are ready to go.
Now we can go out and play."

Spot came in with something.

He ran to Sally.

Sally laughed and laughed.

"Oh, look," she said.

"Spot wants to get ready.

Spot wants to put on something.

He wants to go out and play, too."

Spot Wants to Play

Mother said, "Look, Sally.

Spot wants to play.

Spot wants to run and jump.

He wants to play ball with you."

Sally said, "Go away, Spot.

Mother wants to work.

And I want to work, too.

I do not want to play ball.

I can not play with you now."

Jump, jump went the dog.

Bump, bump went the ball.

Away ran Spot to get it.

He ran and ran with the ball.

Sally said, "No, no, Spot.

Do not run and jump

in the house.

Do not play ball here.

We do not play ball in the house."

Bump, bump went the red ball.
It went to Sally.

Sally said, "Come, Spot.
We will go out and find Puff.
Puff will play ball with you.
I want to work."

Sally went out with the ball.
The little dog went with Sally.
They went to find Puff.

Soon Sally saw Puff.

"Come, Puff," said Sally.

"Spot wants to run and play.

Come and play ball with Spot."

Bump, bump went the red ball.

Jump, jump went Puff and Spot
to get the ball.

Sally ran to the house.

"Now I can work," she said.

"And Spot can play ball
with Puff."

Who Did It?

"Kerchoo!" went Sally.
"Kerchoo, kerchoo!"

"Oh, Sally," said Mother.
"Have you a handkerchief?"

"No, Mother," said Sally.
"I do not have a handkerchief."

"Here, Sally," said Mother.
"Here is one for you."

"Oh, Mother," said Sally.

"Tim wants a handkerchief.

I have a handkerchief.

And Tim wants one, too.

Please get a handkerchief

for Tim."

Mother laughed.

"Funny little Sally," she said.

"Here is a handkerchief for Tim."

Sally went kerchoo.

"Look, Mother," said Sally.

"Guess who went kerchoo."

"My, my," said Mother.

"I see Tim with the handkerchief.

I can guess who went kerchoo.

Tim went kerchoo."

Sally laughed and laughed.

"Oh, yes," said Sally.

"Tim went kerchoo."

What Sally Ate

"Bow-wow," said Spot.

"Oh, Spot," said Sally.

"I see what you see.

It is candy.

Candy is good.

But candy is not good for dogs.

So I will eat it."

Sally ate and ate.

"Oh, my!" she said.

"This candy is good."

Soon Mother came to find Sally.
She came to get Sally
ready for dinner.
Mother did not see the candy.

"Oh, Sally," she said.
"Who ate the candy?
Did Spot eat it?"

Sally said, "I ate it.
Candy is not good for dogs.
So I ate it."

"What a good dinner," said Father.

"What a good dinner," said Dick.

Sally said, "Oh, my.

It is a good dinner.

But I do not want it now."

Mother said, "Sally ate the candy.

Now she can not eat dinner.

But Spot did not eat candy.

So he will eat a good dinner soon."

Good Times
at the
Farm

Dick Comes to the Farm

"Hello, Dick," said Grandfather.
"I came for you in the car.
Guess who came with me."

"I can guess," said Dick.
"It is Grandmother."

They went to the car.
"Hello, hello," said Dick.
"Here is Grandmother.
And here is Don, too."

Soon they came to the farm.

"Now we will have fun," said Don.

"We will work and play."

Dick said, "Yes, we will work and play on the farm.

You have on farm clothes.

I will put on farm clothes, too."

Dick went in the house.

He put on farm clothes, and soon he came out.

Grandmother said, "Look, boys.

I have something here for you.

Two big farm hats.

Two big yellow hats.

One for Don and one for Dick."

"Thank you," said Don.

"Thank you," said Dick.

"Now we have on farm clothes
and farm hats.

Now we are ready to work and
play on the farm."

Too Fast

Up went Don and Dick.

Up, up, up in the barn.

"Look, look," said Don.

"See what I can do.

See me jump down."

Dick said, "I can jump, too.

Here I go.

See me jump down."

The boys saw Black Pony.

"Here is Black Pony," said Don.

"I can ride on Black Pony.

I can ride fast."

Away went Don for a ride.

Dick said, "I want a ride, too.

Look, Grandfather, look."

Away went Dick on Black Pony.

But he went too fast.

Away went the big farm hat.

And down came Dick with a bump.

"Are you hurt?" said Grandfather.

"No, Grandfather," said Dick.

"But my clothes are hurt.

They are black."

"Oh, no," said Grandfather.

"You did not hurt the clothes.

Grandmother can wash the clothes.

And she will wash you, too."

Dick Wants to Play

"Come, boys," said Grandmother.

"You can go to bed now.

The horses and cows are in bed.

The hens and chickens are in bed.

The pets are in bed, too."

Dick said, "Oh, Grandmother.

I do not want to go to bed.

I want to play with the toys.

I want Don to play, too."

But Don was tired.

He went to bed.

Grandmother was tired, and
so was Grandfather.

They went to bed, too.

But Dick did not go to bed.

"Now I will have fun," he said.

"I do not have to go to bed.

Now I will find some toys
to play with."

Dick looked at the toys.

"Here is a big blue ball," he said.

"I like to play ball with Don.

But Don is in bed.

So we can not play ball.

What can I do now?

I can not play with the pets.

I do not want to play with toys.

So I will look at this."

Dick saw a pony.

"This looks like Black Pony," he said.

"And here are some horses.

I see a cow and three ducks.

I see a house, too."

Dick wanted to look and look.

But he was tired.

Dick was too tired to look.

He did not want to go to sleep.

But he did.

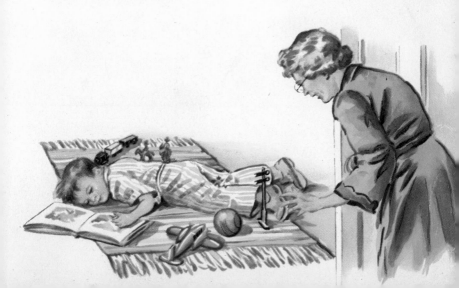

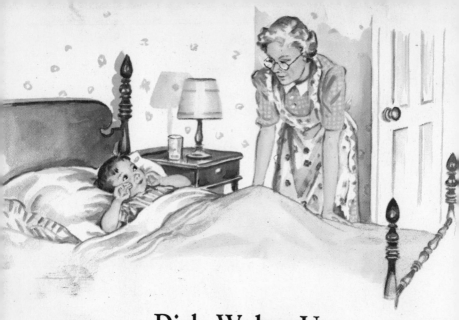

Dick Wakes Up

"Where am I?" said Dick.
"Where am I, Grandmother?"

Grandmother laughed.
"You are in bed," she said.
"You did not want to go to bed.
You wanted to play.
But you went to sleep.
So I put you in bed."

"I will get up now," said Dick.

"The chickens want breakfast.

The ducks want breakfast.

The pets want breakfast.

I want to help you.

I want to help you with the ducks
and the chickens."

Grandmother laughed.

"You are too late," she said.

"You did not wake up.

You can not help me now."

Grandfather came in.

"Oh, Grandfather," said Dick.

"I want to go to the barn.

I want to help you work.

The horses want breakfast.

The cows and pigs want breakfast.

I want to help."

Grandfather said, "No, Dick.

You can not help me now.

You are too late."

"Oh, my!" said Dick.

"I wanted to help you.

But now I am too late to help.

I went to bed late, and

so I did not get up."

"Dick is too late to help,"
said Grandmother.

"But he is not too late

for a good breakfast.

And breakfast is ready now."

The Big Farm Hat

"Here we go," said Dick.

"Here we go," said Don.

"Good-by, Grandmother.

Here we go out to play."

"Oh, Dick," said Grandmother.

"You do not have a hat.

You must put on a hat.

Here is the big yellow hat."

"Look at me," said Don.

"See what I can do.

I can go down.

See me go down, down, down."

Dick said, "That is fun.

I will do that, too."

Don and Dick did not see
White Cow.

But White Cow saw Don.

She saw Dick.

And she saw the big farm hat.

Grandfather saw Don and Dick.

He saw the big farm hat.

And he saw White Cow get
the big farm hat.

Dick went to get the big hat.

But he did not find it.

"Oh, where is my hat?" he said.

"Where is my big yellow hat?"

Grandfather laughed.

"Here is the big hat," he said.

"You did not want it.

But White Cow wanted it.

She wanted it for dinner.

It is a funny hat now."

63

Breakfast at the Barn

Dick and Don went to the barn.

They wanted to see the animals eat breakfast.

They wanted to see Grandfather milk the cows.

"Look at Black Pony," said Dick.

"See Black Pony eat breakfast."

The boys saw Black Pony eat.

They saw the horses eat, too.

Then they saw the cows eat.

And they saw Grandfather
milk the cows.

"I like milk," said Dick.

"So do I," said Don.

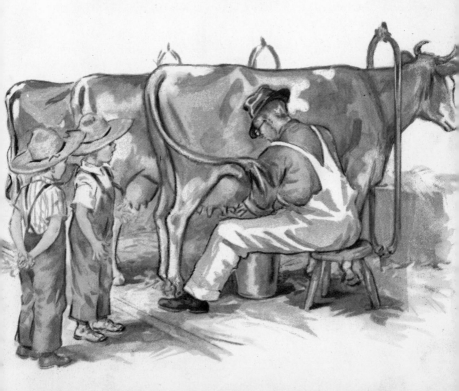

Mother Cat came to the barn
with four little kittens.

They ran to Grandfather.

"Mew, mew," said the mother cat.

"Mew, mew," said the kittens.

"Oh, Grandfather," said Dick.

"Look at the cat and the kittens.

What do they want?"

Grandfather laughed.

He said, "They want breakfast.

And breakfast is ready.

Ready for the cat family."

Dick said, "I see what they want.

They want milk for breakfast.

Boys and girls like milk.

Cats and kittens like it, too."

"Mew, mew," said the kittens.

A Good Breakfast

"Cluck, cluck," said the hens.

"Quack, quack," said the ducks.

"Cluck, cluck, quack, quack," went the hens and the ducks.

Dick said, "Hello, White Hen.
Here is some breakfast for you and the little chickens."

Don said, "Hello, Mother Duck.
Here is some breakfast for you and the duck family."

Dick said, "Now we will find
some eggs for our breakfast.

I like eggs for breakfast."

Soon Don said, "I have three eggs."

Dick said, "I have four eggs.

Put the eggs in my big hat, and
we will go to the house.

Then Grandmother can get
a good breakfast for the family."

The boys saw the mother cat and the kittens.

They wanted to pet the kittens.

So Dick put down the big hat with the eggs in it.

Then a pig saw the eggs in the big farm hat.

And the pig ate the eggs.

"Oh, my!" said Dick.

"Look at my hat!

Where are the eggs?

Who ate the eggs?"

Don looked at the pig.

"It was that pig," he said.

"That pig ate our eggs!"

Dick said, "Animals are funny.

A cow ate my hat for dinner.

A pig ate our eggs for breakfast."

71

Big Dog Helps Dick

"Look, look," said Dick.

"See this funny little pig.

I want to pet it."

"Bow-wow!" said Big Dog.

He wanted to say something

to Dick.

But dogs can not talk.

So he went bow-wow.

Mother Pig ran at the boys.

Dick put down the little pig
and ran away.

Don ran, too.

Big Dog did not run away.

He did not want Mother Pig
to hurt Dick.

So he ran at Mother Pig, and
then she ran away.

"Oh, Dick," said Grandmother.

"You can not pet all the animals.

Some animals will hurt you."

Dick said, "Yes, Grandmother.

Big Dog wanted to say that, too.

He wanted to say that I

must not pet little pigs.

But dogs can not talk.

So he went bow-wow.

Thank you, Big Dog, thank you."

Something for Dinner

Dick said, "Look, look.

Now we have something for dinner.

We must go home now.

We will have a big dinner."

But Don said, "It is not late.

Do not go home now.

This is fun."

So they did not go home then.

"Now we can go home," said Don.

"I have one, two, three.

You have one, two, three, four.

We will have a big, big dinner."

Dick was ready to go home.

Don was ready, too.

Away they went.

On and on went the boys.

Soon Don said, "I am tired.

I want to stop here."

Dick said, "I am tired, too.

And I want to stop.

But we can not stop now.

It is late.

We must get home for dinner."

But Don was too tired to go on.

So he sat down, and Dick

sat down, too.

Then Dick saw a car.
Grandfather was in it.
He said, "You are late.
So I came for you in the car.
Grandmother wants you
to come home for dinner."

"Oh, Grandfather," said Dick.
"We are late.
But see what we have.
Now Grandmother can get
a big, big dinner."

The Family at the Farm

Mother and Father came
to the farm to get Dick.

Jane and Sally came, too.

They wanted to see Grandmother
and Grandfather.

Grandmother said, "All my family
is here.

So I will get a big dinner.

The children can help me."

Dick and Don went to get
eggs for Grandmother.

Jane went to get milk
for Grandmother.

Sally said, "I can get something
for Grandmother, too.

I will go out and find
something for dinner."

And out she went.

Sally looked and looked.

She saw something go hop, hop.

It was a rabbit.

Hop, hop, hop went the rabbit.

Then Sally saw the little rabbit
eat something red.

"Oh," said Sally.

"Here is something to eat.

Rabbits like it.

Grandmother will like it, too."

"Look, Grandmother," said Dick.
"See what we have.
We have some eggs for you."

"Look, Grandmother," said Jane.
"I have some milk for you."

"Oh, Grandmother," said Sally.
"See what I have for you.
It is good to eat.
Rabbits eat it."

Grandmother and Dick laughed.
Don and Jane laughed, too.

"Oh, Sally," said Grandmother.
"Boys and girls do not eat
all that rabbits eat.
But this is pretty to look at.
So I will put it here, and
we can all look at it.
Thank you, Sally, thank you."

Sleep, Sally, Sleep

"What a good dinner," said Mother.
"Now the children must sleep.
And then we will go home."

Dick and Jane wanted to sleep.
But Sally did not want to sleep.

She said, "Oh, Grandfather.
I want to go to the barn.
I want to say good-by to Black Pony.
Then I will sleep."

Sally went out to the barn
with Grandfather.

She said good-by to Black Pony.

"Now we will go to the house,"
said Grandfather.

But Sally said, "I want to see
the cat and the kittens, too.

I want to see the cows and ducks
and the pigs with the funny tails.

I must see the hens and chickens."

She wanted to stop and say good-by
to all the animals.

And that is what she did.

Mother came to get Sally.

"Oh, Sally," she said.

"I wanted you to sleep a little.

But you did not sleep at all.

And now we must go home."

They all said good-by to Don and
Grandmother and Grandfather.

Dick said, "Good-by, good-by.

It was fun to work and play

with you on the farm."

Away they went in the car.

It was fun for Dick and Jane
to ride home.

But it was not fun for Sally.

Sally was tired, and Sally
went to sleep.

Dick and Jane looked here and
looked there.

"See that big red barn," said Jane.

"See that funny dog," said Dick.

On and on went the car.

Dick and Jane saw four rabbits.
They saw a big yellow car
with two horses in it.
They saw cows and chickens.
They saw a big, big boat.

Sally did not wake up.
She did not see the animals.
She did not see the big boat.
She did not see the yellow car
with horses in it.
All Sally did was
sleep and sleep
and sleep.

Good Times
with
Friends

The Birthday Dinner

"My friends are here," said Jane.

"All my friends are ready
for the birthday dinner."

"And the birthday dinner
is ready," said Mother.

Then the children sat down
to eat the dinner.

They ate and ate.

Soon Mother went to get
the cookies and candy.

Sally saw Mother put something
on the cookies.
It was something white.

Sally said, "I will help Mother.
Here is something black.
I will put something black
on the cookies."

Mother said, "Here is the candy.

And here comes little Sally

with the cookies."

Sally said, "Here I come

with the good cookies.

You can have some cookies now."

"Thank you, Sally," said Tom.

"Thank you, Sally," said Jack.

"Thank you, Sally," said Susan.

"Kerchoo!" went Susan.

"Kerchoo!" went Jack and Tom.

"Kerchoo, kerchoo!" went Sally.

And down went the cookies.

Bump, bump, bump.

"Well, well," said Mother.

"What is this?"

Mother looked at the cookies.

"Oh, Sally," she said.

"I see something black
on the cookies.

Did you put something
on the cookies?"

Sally said, "Yes, Mother.
I wanted to help you.
So I put something good
on the cookies."

The New Toy

Jane said, "Hello, Susan.

See my new toy.

It came for my birthday.

I can wash clothes in it.

I have three new dolls, too.

I can wash my doll clothes."

Susan said, "Oh, Jane.

I like to wash doll clothes.

I will help you."

"Now the clothes are clean,"
said Jane.

"We will put the clean clothes
up here."

So they put up the clothes.

Susan said, "It is fun
to wash doll clothes.

I will run home and get some.

I have some doll clothes that
are not clean."

And away she went.

Wash! Wash! Wash!
Soon Jane said, "Well, well.
The doll clothes are all clean.
Now we will stop."

"Yes," said Susan.
"Our doll clothes are clean.
But it is fun to wash clothes.
And I do not want to stop.
What can we wash now?"

Then down, down, down
went the clean doll clothes.
The girls ran to look.
"Oh, my!" said Susan.
"Look at our doll clothes.
They are not clean now."

Jane laughed and laughed.
She said, "Well, Susan.
We did not want to stop our work.
We wanted something to wash.
Now we have something."

Lunch at School

Jane was a happy little girl.

"Oh, Susan," she said.

"I can eat lunch with you.

Mother is not at home.

So I will eat lunch at school.

It is fun to eat at school.

I can get what I like to eat."

Susan was happy, too.

"We can go now," she said.

"We can get our lunch now."

Susan and Jane went to get lunch.

"Here is something good,"
said Susan.

"I will get this."

"And I will get this," said Jane,
"and this and this."

The girls went on.

"Here is something good, too,"
said Susan.

"Now I am ready to eat lunch."

"So am I," said Jane.

The girls sat down to eat.

Susan laughed and laughed.

"Oh, Jane," she said.

"What a funny lunch you have.
You do not eat a lunch like that
at home.

And it is not a good lunch
to eat at school."

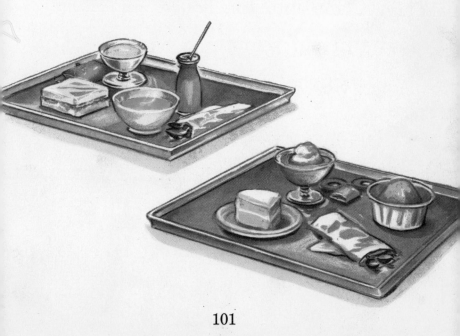

It Hurts

"It hurts!" said Sally.
"Oh, Jane, look at this.
Please put something on it."

Jane said, "I will help you.
Come into the house, and
I will put something on it."
And that is what Jane did.

Then Sally ran out to play.

Spot went, too.

Sally saw the big red ball.

She ran to get it.

And Spot ran to get it, too.

Bump, bump, bump!

Down went Sally.

The ball was under Sally.

And Sally was under Spot.

"Oh, Spot," said Sally.
"Look at this.
See what you did to me."

"Bow-wow," said Spot.

"It hurts," Sally said.
"I must go and put something
on it."
So Sally went into the house.

Sally said, "It hurts here.
And it hurts there.
I will put something on it.
I will put this on it here.
I will put that on it there.
And then it will not hurt."

Please and Thank You

"Hello, children," said Mother.
"I have something for you."
Dick and Jane ran to Mother.

Mother said, "I work at home,
and you work at school.
We are tired now, and our friends
are tired.
We will have something to eat.
Something good.
And our friends will eat, too."

All the children sat down to eat.
They ate and ate and ate.

Jack said, "I like animal cookies."
Susan said, "Here is a cookie pig
with a funny tail."
Tom said, "Quack, quack.
See my cookie duck."

Sally said, "I have a hen.
But it can not say cluck, cluck."

Spot sat up.

"Bow-wow," he said.

Tom said, "Look at Spot.

Spot wants something to eat.

He can not talk, but he

can say please."

Mother laughed.

"Here, Spot," she said.

"You said please.

So you can have a cookie.

I will get you a cookie rabbit."

Spot ate the cookie rabbit.

Tom said, "Look at Spot now.

See that funny tail.

See that funny tail go.

Spot can not talk.

But he can say thank you

with that funny tail."

"Children can talk," said Susan.

"We want to say thank you, too.

Thank you for this good lunch."

Sally Rides Fast

"Good-by, Sally," said Jack.

"Good-by, Sally," said Dick.

But Sally did not say good-by.

She wanted to go with the boys.

"I will go, too," she said.

"I can go for a ride.

I can go in my little car."

"Oh, Sally," said the boys.

"Please go home."

Dick said, "We want to have fun.

We want to go fast.

But you can not go fast."

"Yes, I can," said Sally.

"You will see.

I can go fast in my car."

Away went the boys.

Fast, fast, fast!

Away went Sally.

Fast, fast, fast!

Bump went the little car.

And out went Sally.

She was too little to go fast.

Sally was not hurt.

But she was not happy.

Jack saw Sally.

"Stop, Dick, stop," he said.

Then Dick saw Sally, too.

He said, "We must help Sally.

Funny little Sally.

She wants to go fast."

Jack said, "Come, Sally.

I will help you get in here."

Away went Dick and Jack and
little Sally.

Away they all went.

Fast, fast, fast!

And now Sally was happy.

Sally saw Mother, and she saw
some friends.

"Look at me," she said.
"I am a big girl now.
I can go fast, too!"

The Birthday Doll

"Oh, Baby Doll," said Jane.

"You are clean and pretty.

You have pretty clothes, too."

Jane put down the birthday doll.

"Ma-ma, ma-ma," it said.

Jane said, "Oh, Baby Doll.

I must go to lunch now.

But I will come out and

play with you soon."

Spot wanted to play with Jane.

But she was not there.

Dick was not there, and Sally was not there.

Then he saw Baby Doll.

The little dog wanted to play with something.

So he ran away with Baby Doll.

He ran into the play house.

Jane ate lunch.

Then she came out to play
with the new doll.

She did not find it.

Jane looked and looked.

But she did not find Baby Doll.

Then something said, "Ma-ma,
ma-ma, ma-ma."

Jane ran to the play house.

There was Spot with the doll.

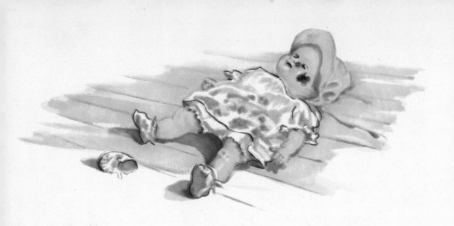

Jane looked at the new doll.

It did not look new and clean.

It did not look happy.

"Oh, Spot!" said Jane.

"See what you did to my doll.

I was not good to my baby.

I was not a good mother.

I did not put my baby away."

"Ma-ma," said Baby Doll.

"Ma-ma, ma-ma."

Jane ran into the house
with Baby Doll.

She said, "I will wash Baby Doll.

I will wash the doll clothes.

Then Baby Doll will look pretty.

She will look clean and new."

And soon Jane was happy.

Baby Doll was pretty and clean.

She looked like new.

"Ma-ma, ma-ma," she said.

Stop and Go

"Here we go," said Dick.

"Here we go for a fast ride."

Away went Dick and Jane
and Sally.

"Look out, Jack!" they said.

But Jack did not look.

And bump!

They ran into Jack.

Down went Jack, and out went
all the children.

Jack was under Dick.

Jane was under Sally.

Sally was under Tim.

But no one was hurt.

They laughed and laughed.

Sally ran into the house.

And soon little Sally came out
with a big red handkerchief.

Jane saw Sally come out
with the big red handkerchief.

"Oh, Sally," she said.

"What will you do with that?"

Sally said, "You will see.

You and Dick and Jack must go
for a ride.

Then you will see what I do
with the big red handkerchief."

"Here we go," said Dick.

"Here we go for a fast ride."

Away went Dick, Jane, and Jack.

Soon they came to Sally.

They laughed and laughed.

"Oh, Sally," they said.

"We can see now.

We see what you wanted to do

with the big red handkerchief."

To the Teacher

Good Times with Our Friends is designed for six-year-olds and follows the Primer *Happy Days* in the Health and Personal Development Program of the Curriculum Foundation Series. The important concepts of health, safety, and personal development are listed on pages 125-128. All words in *Good Times*, except the 100 listed below, are words used in the preceding book in this program, *Happy Days*. For children who have completed The New Basic Reading Program, *Fun with Dick and Jane* (Primer), only the 18 words printed in boldface type in the list below will be new.

Vocabulary List

Unit I
6 **wake**
  she
7 **breakfast**
8 eat
9 went
  bow-wow
10 **ready**
  wash
11 —
12 now
13 but
14 soon
15 —
16 yes
17 this
  good
18 too
19 a
20 **milk**
  please
21 away
  four
22 red
  hurt
23 —
24 my
25 **lunch**
  cookies
26 **some**
27 saw
  Tim
28 ate
  boat
29 —
30 who
  baby
31 —

32 yellow
  white
33 **put**
  on
34 ran
35 run
  ball
36 dog
  bump
37 find
  they
38 —
39 **handkerchief**
40 —
41 —
42 **candy**
  so
43 **dinner**
44 —

Unit II
46 farm
  grandmother
47 **clothes**
48 **hats**
49 fast
  barn
50 black
  pony
51 —
52 cows
  pets
53 was
  tired
54 looked
  at
55 ducks
  wanted
56 am

57 **late**
58 pigs
59 —
60 good-by
  must
61 that
62 —
63 —
64 animals
65 **then**
66 cat
  mew
67 family
  girls
68 cluck
  quack
69 eggs
  our
70 —
71 —
72 say
  talk
73 —
74 all
75 home
76 —
77 sat
78 —
79 children
80 —
81 hop
  rabbit
82 —
83 —
84 —
85 tails
86 —
87 there
88 —

Unit III
90 birthday
  friends
91 —
92 Tom
93 well
94 —
95 dolls
96 **clean**
97 —
98 —
99 happy
  school
100 —
101 —
102 into
103 under
104 —
105 —
106 —
107 —
108 —
109 —
110 —
111 —
112 —
113 —
114 —
115 ma-ma
116 —
117 —
118 —
119 —
120 —
121 —
122 —
123 —

Important Health, Safety, and Personal Development Concepts
Introduced in *Good Times with Our Friends*

Good Times with Our Friends is a health book especially designed for six-year-olds. It centers around the known health needs of this age group. Among these needs are: guidance in working and playing safely, since Six is an age when the accident rate goes up; realization of the importance of sleep to general health and to the disposition and a willingness to observe reasonable-bedtime hours; appreciation of the values of milk, a food six-year-olds sometimes dismiss as "baby-food"; willingness to at least *try* new foods instead of spurning them in typical six-year-old fashion; appreciation of the need to use a handkerchief when coughing or sneezing, as a means of curbing the spread of cold germs which attack six-year-olds all too frequently; motivation to help themselves in so far as possible in dressing, washing, combing and brushing hair, taking care of the teeth, eating a good breakfast (their poorest meal), in learning to get along happily with family members and with youngsters their own age.

All these needs are taken into account in *Good Times*. In fact, research done in preparation for this and other books in the Health and Personal Development Program[1] is embodied in a companion book for teachers and parents—a text in child growth and development entitled *These Are Your Children*.[2] This research is also reviewed in brief form in the complete *Guidebook* for teachers which accompanies *Good Times*.

In working toward the major goal of all health teaching—that of translating health knowledge into improved health behavior—the Health and Personal Development Program foregoes the use of the expository style of writing until later levels in the pupils' books. Thus *Good Times* features realistic, easy-to-read stories with provocative health themes—stories highly charged with interest and capable of motivating young children to discuss and to *do* the safe, kindly, healthful things they should do. In utilizing the story approach for beginners in the health field—and in presenting in the stories true-to-life child characters, problems, and situations—*Good Times* reflects a viewpoint emphasized in the joint NEA-AMA yearbook *Health Education*,[3] namely that desired outcomes in health teaching can come only from health education based on "real problems, real people, and real situations."

---

[1]*Happy Days*, a Primer, and *Good Times*, *Three Friends*, *Five in the Family*, *The Girl Next Door*, *You, You and Others*, *You're Growing Up*, and *Into Your Teens*, for Grades One through Eight. Scott, Foresman and Company.
[2]*These Are Your Children* by Gladys G. Jenkins, Helen Shacter, and W. W. Bauer. Expanded Edition. Scott, Foresman and Company. 1953.
[3]*Health Education*, Joint Yearbook of the NEA-AMA. Fourth Edition. Washington, D.C. The National Education Association. 1948.

UNIT ONE—Good Times at Home

Sally Gets Up (pages 6-9)
Health: Six-year-olds need eleven or twelve hours of sleep each night. Failure to get enough sleep often makes getting up the next morning very difficult.
Personal Development: Getting up promptly is one way of helping keep things "running smoothly" in the prebreakfast period.

Sally Helps Spot (pages 10-13)
Health: Desirable morning routine includes going to the toilet, washing* the hands, brushing the teeth, and combing the hair. Washing the hands before eating is an especially good habit. Leads are given for discussing the desirability of using one's own towel and washcloth. A film children will enjoy at this point is *Patty Gurman, Little Helper* (Frith Films), which follows six-year-old Patty through a typical day.

Ready for Breakfast (pages 14-16)
Personal Development: The ability to assume responsibility for dressing oneself increases with age. Six-year-olds can usually do a good job of it if they try. Promptness in getting ready in the morning is aided by having clean clothes laid out at night— and by having toilet articles in a place where they can be found readily.

Eat It and See (pages 17-19)
Health: Meals are more enjoyable when they include new foods now and then.
Personal Development: "Eat it and see" is usually a good way to approach new foods.

Spot and the Cars (pages 20-24)
Safety: Even in emergencies, traffic signals should be obeyed. These signals include the green, yellow, and red traffic lights as well as the traffic directions given by policemen and patrol boys.

Milk Is Good (pages 25-27)
Health: Milk is one of the most important foods in the diet, and boys and girls need about three or four glasses of it every day. Part of this amount may be obtained in milk dishes; e.g., puddings and cream soups. Further interest in milk may be aroused by showing a film like *The Dairy Farm* (Coronet Films) or by visiting a local dairy.

What Sally Saw (pages 28-30)
Health: Keeping reasonably clean is not only a good health habit, but it adds considerably to our personal appearance. Washing after eating is often desirable, especially after eating "sticky" foods.

Ready for Play (pages 31-34)
Health: Proper clothing protects us against the weather. Different kinds of clothing are necessary in different kinds of weather.

Spot Wants to Play (pages 35-38)
Safety: Strenuous games such as playing ball are better carried on outdoors.
Personal Development: Being resourceful often helps in overcoming annoyances.

Who Did It? (pages 39-41)
Health: The proper use of the handkerchief when coughing or sneezing will help prevent the spread of germs that cause colds and other diseases.

What Sally Ate (pages 42-44)
Health: Sweet foods, especially candy, eaten before meals tend to spoil the appetite. It is best to eat sweets as a dessert after meals. Good between-meal snacks are fruit or fruit juices, oatmeal cookies, and popcorn.

UNIT TWO—Good Times at the Farm

Dick Comes to the Farm (pages 46-48)
Health: Although we all need sunshine, too much of it at one time can cause severe sunburn. Providing adequate protection is a sensible precaution.
Personal Development: Learning to dress appropriately is a part of "growing up." Six-year-olds can assume some responsibility for selecting suitable clothes.

Too Fast (pages 49-51)
Safety: There is need for using common sense in play. Recklessness and "showing off" may lead to unpleasant results.
Personal Development: It is all right to get dirty if properly dressed for play.

Dick Wants to Play (pages 52-55)
Health: Getting enough sleep is important to growing strong and keeping healthy. Leads for discussing desirable bedtime routine.
Personal Development: Nothing—not even play—seems much fun when we are tired! Loss of sleep may leave us "cross" and without our usual pep.

Dick Wakes Up (pages 56-59)
Health: Leads for reviewing the concept that six-year-olds need eleven or twelve hours of sleep each night.
Personal Development: "Oversleeping" may result in missing out on some fun. And it almost always causes confusion and a "bad start" to the day.

The Big Farm Hat (pages 60-63)
Health: Sunshine is necessary for life, but moderation and gradual exposure to the sun's rays are desirable. Youngsters will enjoy hearing you read aloud some of the fascinating material from Herbert Zim's *The Sun* (Morrow).
Personal Development: Carelessness with one's possessions is likely to produce unhappy results.

Breakfast at the Barn (pages 64-67)
Health: All living things need foods that are appropriate for them. People need such foods as milk, bread, butter (or margarine), cereal, meat (or fish or eggs), potatoes, fruit, and green and yellow vegetables each day. Children are interested in the story of foods and this is a good place to read aloud such books as *This Is the Bread That Betsy Ate* by Irma S. Black (William R. Scott).

A Good Breakfast (pages 68-71)
Health: Breakfast is an important meal since it comes after many hours of not eating. A good breakfast is one that helps supply the body with important foods it needs, such as bread or toast, butter, fruit, cereal, milk, and sometimes eggs or bacon.
Personal Development: When we have a job to do, we should make every effort to do it as well and as carefully as we can.

Big Dog Helps Dick (pages 72-74)
Safety: It is not safe to pet animals that are not really pets.

Something for Dinner (pages 75-78)
Health: Daily exercise is important (one to two hours a day), but overdoing it often results in fatigue and irritability.

The Family at the Farm (pages 79-83)
Safety: We should not eat things unless we know they are safe and healthful.
Personal Development: Family gatherings and family activities make life interesting and "lots more fun."

Sleep, Sally, Sleep (pages 84-88)
Health: All children, big and little, need rest during the day. Taking a short rest after meals is a very good plan.

UNIT THREE—Good Times with Friends

The Birthday Dinner (pages 90-94)
Health: Leads for discussing desirable types of party menus.
Personal Development: It's fun to help—but there are times when guidance is needed.

The New Toy (pages 95-98)
Health: Reasonable cleanliness is desirable—but overfussiness should be avoided.
Personal Development: Sometimes we must try to make the best of an unfortunate happening. A sense of humor usually helps.

Lunch at School (pages 99-101)
Health: We need to eat a variety of foods each day. Desserts are all right in their place but not as an entire meal. Leads for setting up samples of desirable lunches.

It Hurts (pages 102-105)
Safety: First Aid—cuts or other breaks in the skin should be reported to parents or other adults promptly so that proper treatment can be given. (Note: Sally dramatizes the concept that first-aid kits and medicines should be kept out of reach of children. Even six-year-olds need adult guidance for medication.)

Please and Thank You (pages 106-109)
Personal Development: Both words and actions can express appreciation. Mothers and fathers plan many good times for their children. A good film to show in this connection is *Courtesy for Beginners* (Coronet Films).

Sally Rides Fast (pages 110-114)
Safety: Trying to do what older and more skillful children do is not always safe.
Personal Development: Older children should assume some responsibility for their younger brothers and sisters. The knowledge that younger children admire and look up to them often helps older boys and girls assume this responsibility gracefully. A story you might read aloud here is *Big Brother Danny* by Jean Fiedler (Holiday House).

The Birthday Doll (pages 115-119)
Health: Leads for reviewing times when cleanliness is necessary; e.g., in getting ready for school, before meals, after play periods, before bed.
Personal Development: Assuming the blame for one's own carelessness is better than making alibis or blaming others. Finding ways to meet problems is preferable to sulking, "getting mad," or just giving up in a difficult or unexpected situation.

Stop and Go (pages 120-123)
Safety: Playing on the sidewalk with vehicles such as wagons or bicycles calls for carefulness and for following such safety rules as keeping to the right of the walk, traveling at "a safe speed," avoiding riding two abreast, and keeping the walk clear of toys not in use. Leads for considering safety precautions en route to school, on the school playground, and in school.
Personal Development: Friendly coöperation in play may prevent accidents and injuries. There is satisfaction in considering the welfare of others.